INSIDE...

£7.99

ALL WEBBED UP!

SPIDEY HAS TO FORM WEBBING BARRIERS TO STOP SANDMAN FROM CATCHING FLASH, BUT HE'S ONLY GOT ENOUGH LEFT TO MAKE 5!

DRAW UP TO 5 WEBBING BARRIERS IN THE CIRCLES ON THE MAZE TO BLOCK THE ROUTE FROM SANDMAN TO FLASH!

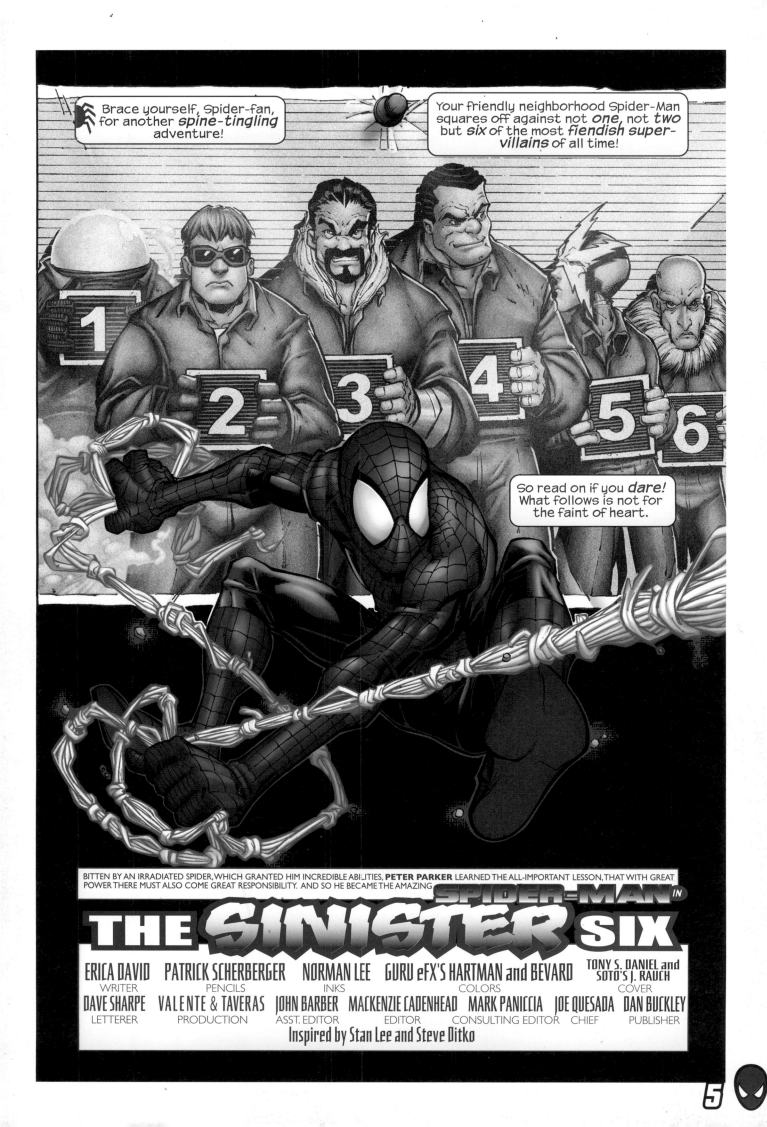

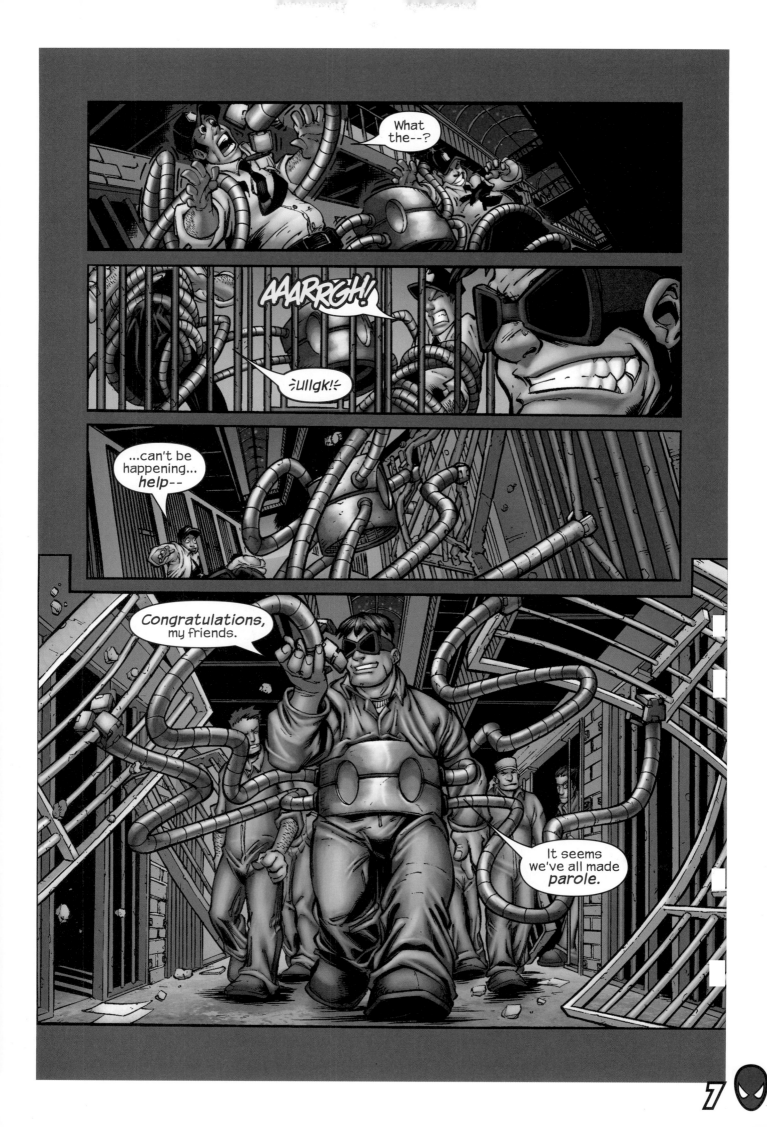

CONTINUED ON PAGE 12

FULLY ARMED

1. DRAW TWO LINES WITH A CIRCLE ON THE END TO GET THE BASIC SHAPE.

2. ADD 3 SPIKES TO EACH CIRCLE, LIKE THIS.

3. FINISH THE DETAIL ON THE SPIKES, AND ADD THE JOIN DETAILS TO THE ARM.

TIP: LEAVE SOME WHITE BITS ON THE ARMS TO MAKE THEM LOOK LIKE SHINY METAL!

STEP **5** Finally, add some colour, using this picture as a guide!

STEP **4** Go over your final picture with pen.

11

CONTINUED FROM PAGE 9

CONTINUED ON PAGE 19

17

SKETCH FEST: ELECTRO

Check it out spider fans! I've managed to corner Electro so you guys can practise sketching him. You'd better make it quick though before he blasts a hole in the page with his bolts!

Copy this image of Electro, square by square, into the empty grid below. When you're done, grab your pens and pencils and colour him in!

COLOUR GUIDE!

CONTINUED FROM PAGE 17

CONTINUED ON PAGE 30

EYE SPIDEY!

Doc Ock is proving a real handful this time and I'm going to need your help to get out of his clutches!

That tentacled lunatic has faked one of these snaps! Take a look at the photos and see if you can spot ten differences between them!

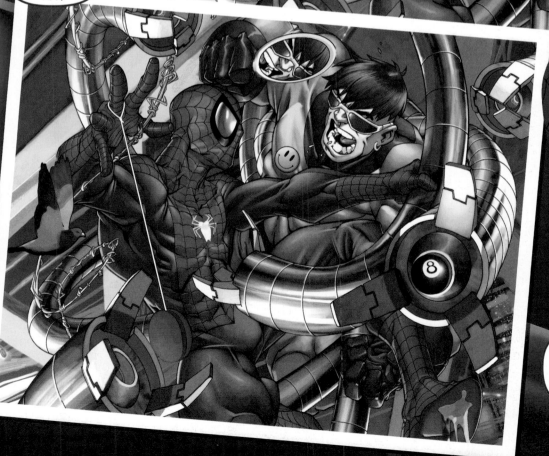

YOU'VE MESSED WITH ME FOR THE LAST TIME, *SPIDER-PEST*. PREPARE TO BE SQUASHED LIKE THE BUG YOU ARE!

WOAH, TAKE A CHILL PILL DOC! NO NEED TO GET YOUR *TENTACLES* IN A TWIST!

ANSWERS: Mirror next to Doc's face; colour of Doc's glasses; extra tentacle in top right of picture; earring on Doc; badge on Doc; 8 ball on tentacle; Spidey's yoyo; pigeon on left of picture; chewing gum on Spidey's shoe.

FROM SAND WEAPONS TO SANDSTORMS - CHECK OUT OUR TOP 5 REASONS WHY TAKING ON THE SANDMAN IS A WHOLE LOT WORSE THAN A BAD DAY AT THE BEACH!

TOP 5 SAND

1 DEADLY WEAPONS

When a nuclear blast ripped through the body of brutal criminal *Flint Marko*, he became bonded with the radioactive sand around him, forming *the Sandman* - a man monster, able to mold his form into any shape imaginable... including *Spidey* smashing weapons!

2 HARD RAIN

The Sandman's mind continues to be in control of his body at all times, no matter how far away it is scattered, so he's able to fire off particles of sand at such a speed that they strike with the force of a vicious hailstorm. And you thought the weather in England was bad!

MAN ATTACKS!

3 ROCK SOLID

The Sandman can also alter the density of different parts of his body however he wants. So even the strongest of Spidey's punches can pass right through his body, whilst his fists stay rock hard, ready to pound the wall-crawler into next week!

4 QUICKSAND

Having weapons for fists is all well and good, but pesky targets like Spidey just won't stand still long enough to use them! No problem for the Sandman - he can pin the web-slinger down under a torrent of sand to keep him still, or just use the sandy quagmire to suffocate him!

5 SANDSTORM

If all else fails for this oversized kitty-litter filler, he can suffocate and blind his enemies by turning his entire body into a lethal sandstorm, allowing him to escape to fight another day, or disorientating them enough for him to launch another round of beach-based brutality!

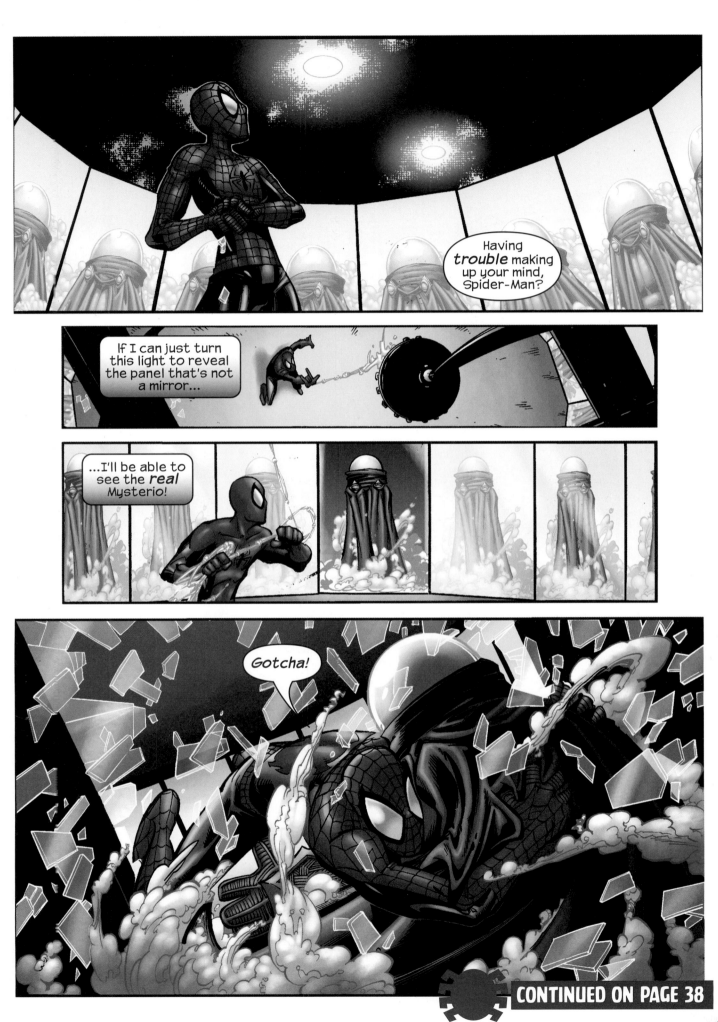

CONTINUED ON PAGE 38

35

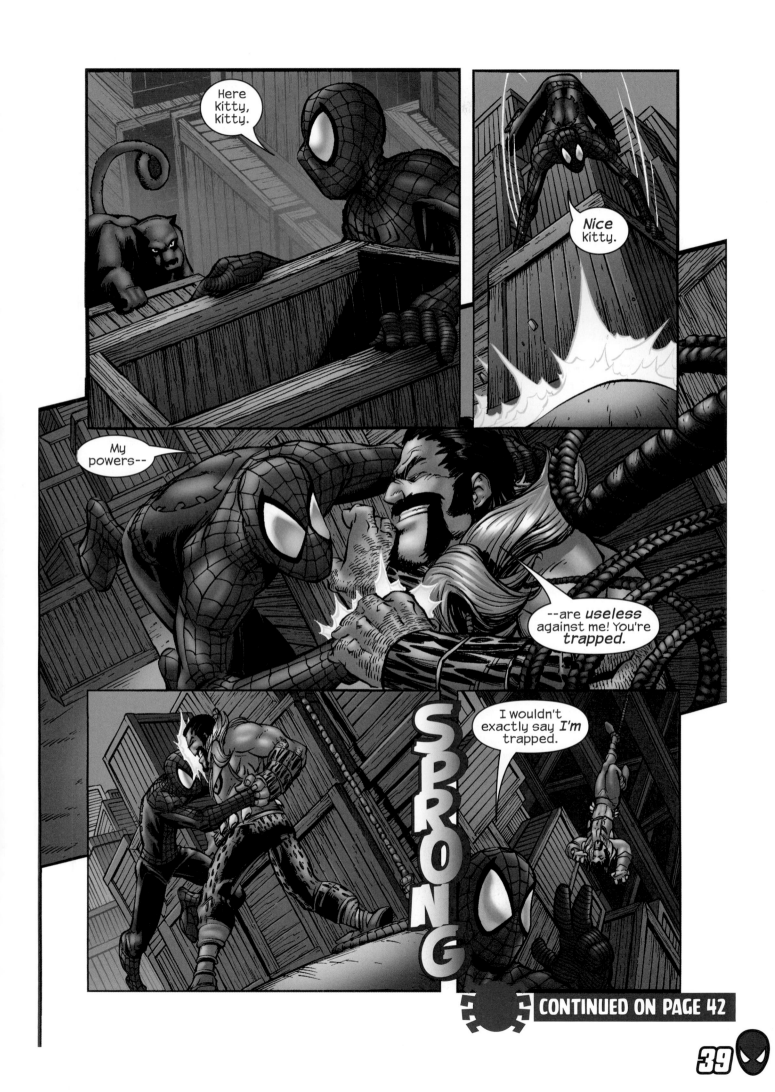

CONTINUED ON PAGE 42

SPIDER FILE:

ELECTRO

DANGER! HIGH VOLTAGE!

Bored with his mundane job as an electrician, **Max Dillon** craved a more exciting life. His prayers were answered when a bolt of lightning struck the power lines he was busy working on. Somehow the jolt of energy altered his body chemistry and gave him the amazing ability to control electricity.

No way.

HUMAN DYNAMO!

Turning his back on his old life, **Dillon** embraced his new abilities and used them to become a super villain. He renamed himself **ELECTRO** and began a devastating crimespree, using his electrical powers to steal anything he desired!

The electricity flowing through his muscles boosts Electro's strength, making him strong enough to lift over 450 pounds.

SHREEAAKT!

From now on, it's all about ELECTRO!!

He might have a pretty goofy looking costume, but laugh at Electro at your peril! Read on to find out all about this shocking Super Villain!

If someone touches Electro when he's fully charged, they will receive a painful blast of electricity!

⭐ SPECIAL MOVES	14
🔴 SPEED	11
⚙️ INTELIGENCE	9
⚡ STRENGTH	10
💥 DAMAGE	16

VILLAIN RATING

60

Electro can supercharge his blasts by drawing power from nearby machinery.

His powers also give him a high voltage shield that can deflect energy blasts!

He can fly through the air by riding upon a wave of electrical energy!

Shocking, isn't it?

You don't know the half of it.

FIRST APPEARANCE

First Appearance: Amazing Spider-Man #9 (1964)

41

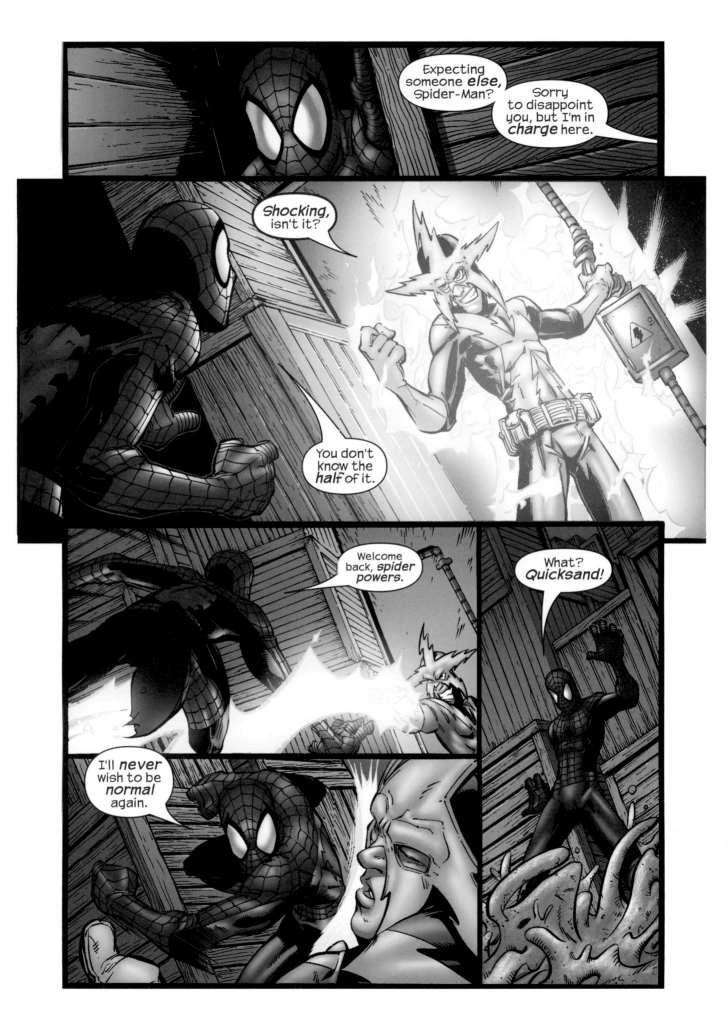

43

CONTINUED ON PAGE 50

47

IT'S NO ACCIDENT THAT THIS AIRBORNE ASSASSIN IS NAMED AFTER ONE OF THE DEADLIEST SCAVENGERS ALIVE. READ ON TO FIND OUT 5 REASONS WHY!

THE VU

1 VENGEANCE

ADRIAN TOOMES BECAME *THE VULTURE* WHEN HE USED HIS FLYING HARNESS TO TAKE REVENGE ON A BUSINESS PARTNER WHO BETRAYED HIM. THE SENSE OF POWER THIS GAVE HIM MADE HIM A MERCILESS FIGHTER, HUNTING TO FEED A RAVENOUS APPETITE FOR WEALTH, POWER AND REVENGE.

2 INTELLIGENCE

HE MAY BE PACKING A HEFTY PAIR OF WINGS, BUT *THE VULTURE* IS ANYTHING BUT BIRD-BRAINED. HE'S INCREDIBLY CUNNING, AND HAS ALSO USED HIS SMARTS TO INVENT AN *ELECTRO-MAGNETIC BODY HARNESS* THAT ALLOWS HIM TO FLY!

3 SPEED

THE VULTURE'S HARNESS CAN LIFT HIM TO A HEIGHT OF 11,500 *FEET*, AND PROPEL HIM THROUGH THE AIR AT A TOP SPEED OF 93MPH. SO KEEP YOUR EYES ON THE SKIES, COS THIS BIRD OF PREY COULD STRIKE FROM ANYWHERE, AT ANY TIME!

LTURE

THE VULTURE'S WING TIPS ARE ALSO RAZOR SHARP, AND CAN EASILY SLICE THROUGH SPIDEY'S WEBBING.

4 AGILITY

HE MAY LOOK LIKE **PROFESSOR X'S** LONG LOST DAD, BUT THIS FEATHERED FIEND IS NO SLOUCH. HIS IMPRESSIVE WINGS AND NATURAL AGILITY MEAN HE CAN MAKE SEEMINGLY IMPOSSIBLE TWISTS AND TURNS AT BREAKNECK SPEED.

5 STRENGTH

THERE'S MORE TO THIS CROOK THAN SPEED AND AGILITY - THE ANTI-GRAVITY WAVES EMITTED BY THE VULTURE'S FLYING HARNESS ALSO BOOST HIS STRENGTH, MAKING HIM STRONGER THAN AN OLYMPIC WEIGHTLIFTER!

CONTINUED ON PAGE 56

THE SINISTER 6 NEED YOU!

Greetings, worms! We're looking for a new member to turn the SINISTER SIX into the SINISTER SEVEN! Think you're evil enough to join our gang? Take this test to find out!

Whilst walking down the street you spot a kitten stuck up a tree do you?

A) Keep on walking - you're too mean to care about one little kitten!
B) Rescue the kitten, find out who owns it and then hold it to ransom!
C) Help the kitten down, and then spend the afternoon tracking down its owner.

The Sinister Six are battling Spidey and the wall-crawling weasel has just fired a barrage of webbing at Dr Octopus. Do you...

A) Dive in front of the webbing to protect Doc Ock!
B) Leg it! With Spidey's attention on Doc Ock, you can escape with the loot from your latest heist!
C) Help Spidey take down the rest of the Sinister Six!

Another group of super villains are putting together a gang and want you to join. What do you do?

A) Tell them no way! You're already a member of the meanest gang around!
B) Tell them you'll work with them but only if they make you the gang's leader!
C) Decline their offer, then contact Spidey to warn him about the new gang!

Okay, your first task is to come up with a really nasty plan. What is it?

A) Run down the high street in your scary costume terrifying all the shoppers!
B) Raid every bank in New York, leaving everyone penny-less except you!
C) Organise a fun day and give all the money raised to charity!

Which of these costumes would you like to wear as a member of the Sinister Six?

A.

B.

C.

Uh-oh! The latest plan has failed and now you're being questioned by the police. What do you say to them?

A) Don't say a word – soon your fellow villains will be along to bust you out of jail... won't they?
B) Nothing! Instead, take the interrogator hostage and make your escape!
C) Explain everything – including how you helped capture the Sinister Six!

HOW DID YOU DO?

MOSTLY As...

Excellent! I can see you're just the kind of villain we're looking for. Welcome to the Sinister Seven!

MOSTLY Bs...

Hmm... You're evil enough, but you're a little too clever for your own good – I want a loyal soldier not a rival leader. I'll be keeping a close eye on you...

MOSTLY Cs...

What?! Your ineptitude makes Frog Man look like a criminal genius! Get out of my sight you simpering do-gooder!

CONTINUED FROM PAGE 53

Later...

ESCAPE ROUTE!

SPIDEY

IT'S TIME TO HELP SPIDEY AS HE COMES FACE TO FACE WITH THE VULTURE!

START

FINISH

CAN YOU FIND A ROUTE FROM SPIDEY TO HIS CLOTHES THAT AVOIDS ALL OF THE VULTURE'S HIDING PLACES?

60

CENTRAL!

CODE CRACKING!

LOOKS LIKE VULTURE DROPPED A SCRAP OF PAPER WITH THE NEXT PLACE HE'S ROBBING ON IT, BUT IT'S CODED!

TQBSLMFT KFXFMMFSZ TUPSF

REPLACE EACH LETTER WITH THE ONE BEFORE IT IN THE ALPHABET TO CRACK THE CODE!

....
....

DOUBLE VISION!

CAN YOU FIND ALL OF THE BIRD NAMES IN THE WORD GRID BELOW?

FALCON ☐
HAWK ☐
EAGLE ☐
CUCKOO ☐
DOVE ☐
OWL ☐
PIGEON ☐
ROBIN ☐
PARROT ☐
PELICAN ☐

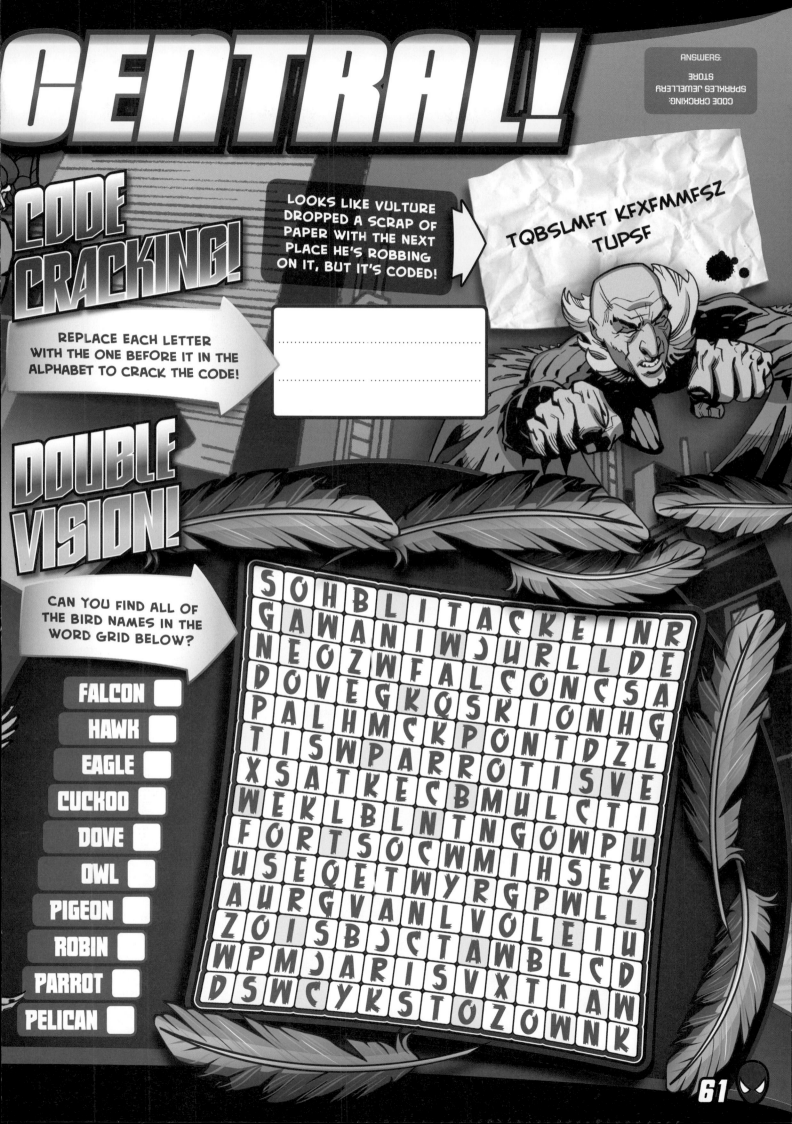

EYE SPIDEY!

THAT *PATHETIC* DEVICE WON'T WORK AGAIN, *BUG*. MY HARNESS IS NOW SPECIALLY SHIELDED AGAINST YOUR *FOOLISH* TOYS!

DON'T WORRY, BALDY. I'VE GOT A WHOLE *LOAD* MORE TRICKS UP MY SLEEVE TO SEND YOU *BACK* TO THE BIRDCAGE!